KINDERGO

Creating Magical Reading Moments

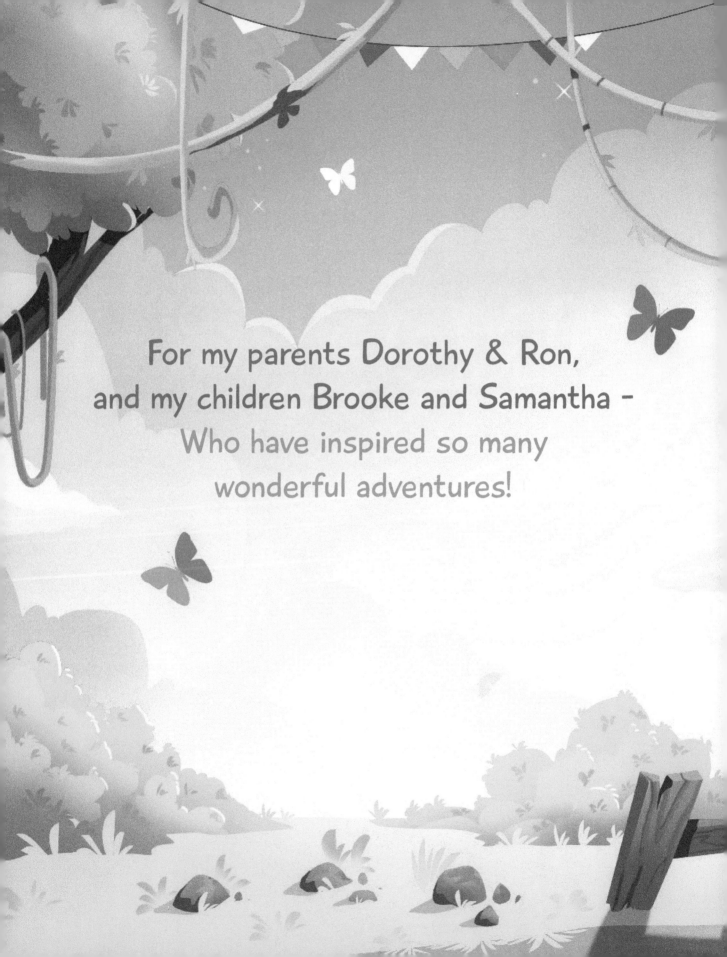

For my parents Dorothy & Ron,
and my children Brooke and Samantha -
Who have inspired so many
wonderful adventures!

The Adventure Birthday Party

Written by:
Barbara J. Bryan
Illustrated by:
Alina Beserman

At last, the big day had arrived.
It was Sam and Brooke's
Birthday Party!

Birthday
5
Years
Sam & Brooke
Saturday 18th September
1246 Elm Lane

The girls greeted their guests eagerly, "Welcome to the Adventure Birthday Party! We are your guides."

First we must cross a great big swamp. Hop across and don't look back, Lest you become a crocodile snack!

Next let's creep into the jungle...
Quiet now, don't make a sound,
There could be tigers all around!

Then it's time for a gondola ride.
Just climb aboard-enjoy the view,
There's deep dark canyons and
mountains too!

Swing along like monkeys
in the trees!
Dangling from the branches,
oh so tall;
Swing so freely, careful
not to fall.

Up to the treehouse we shall climb.
A pirate feast in the sky!
A well earned break, way up high.

Then we fly down the
jungle chute.
The fastest way down
from the tree.
Put your hands up and cry
weeeeeeeee!

Lastly, the rapids.
Jump aboard a sturdy boat,
For down the river we
must float!

It's time to go -
but come back soon.
The Adventure Birthday Party
is here to stay,
So we can play another day!

The End

Lightning Source UK Ltd.
Milton Keynes UK
UKHW051906280119
336353UK00001B/30/P